The
Poem Box

Bitham Brook
Primary School

Other Poetry by Stanley Cook

The Squirrel in Town
The Dragon on the Wall

The
Poem Box

Stanley Cook

Illustrated by George Buchanan

Blackie

To Sarah, Paul and Ann

Copyright © 1991 Stanley Cook
Illustrations © 1991 George Buchanan
First published 1991 by Blackie and Son Ltd

A CIP catalogue record for this book is
available from the British Library.

ISBN 0216 930995

Blackie and Son Ltd
7 Leicester Place
London WC2H 7BP

Printed in Great Britain by
Thomson Litho Ltd, East Kilbride, Scotland

Introduction

'All the world's a stage' and the newspapers and television do their best to decide for us what is being acted in the adult theatre and who are the main performers. Sometimes a natural disaster is on, sometimes a trial, sometimes peace, sometimes war, to give a few stock examples. The media decide when something has run long enough and it disappears from screen and front page overnight. Children, happily for them, put on their own plays.

It does not need much observation of small children to see that grave issues of family, school and national life pass over their heads, even though they may eventually suffer their effects. They have chosen their own actors and given them their own parts in their own story. If Teddy, for example, is there, we can assume he is an actor, though there is a strong possibility he is not playing the part of a Teddy. He will have a great deal to say, all of it unspoken. The action in which he is involved gives some indication of what the answer is, but finding out what the question was is another matter. Like Joyce's *Finnegan's Wake* the story is circular: at the end you go back to the beginning and understand more each time round.

Poems for young children have to fit into what they are already imagining. It is with them as it is with adults: a poem can tell them only what they already know. The reader (or hearer) may not have previously actually thought, let alone put into words, what the poet says, but the poet has the words to bring it to the surface. It was there, just as a number of other calculations were there in two and two make four.

It is fascinating to discover, from some sudden announcement or chance remark, what part Teddy *is* playing. The background of his story (supposing it is revealed) can be just as intriguing. Some years, for example, seem to elapse in a child's life before trees, shrubs and bushes are simply trees, shrubs and bushes, very like others of their kind. In the meantime they are all kinds of places, with brickwork of leaves and girdering of trunk and branches, that fit a story. They also have a personality or presence: read the lines,

> *Under the greenwood tree*
> *Who loves to lie with me,*
> *And turn his merry note*
> *Unto the sweet bird's throat*

and make a snap decision as to what kind of tree it is and then try to think back to when it became your first choice. I guess an oak and remember one oak from my childhood that, to me then, was the actual oak from every fairy tale I knew that involved one. Somewhere at the back of my mind I have never completely accepted that the other (Major) oak in Sherwood Forest was the one Robin Hood used.

It would be a mistake for adults to pride themselves on a more scientific approach. How many people who have sat beneath an oak could have said which of the forty-five species listed in Alan Mitchell's *Field Guide* it was? How many people on any given bus could take the engine to pieces and, after the parts had been shuffled, put it together again? We live in a specialised world where the essential apparatus of everyday life is beyond our individual understanding. If we choose to admit it, our map of our own known world is basically similar to the child's: everything has a 'feel' for us. Our feeling is computed within us from a larger range of more sophisticated items, but like the child we try out on each new thing the assortment of knowledge and pattern of mind that we have. Ideally a poem uses nothing that was not already either in the subject or in the child's mind. A poem is a box with ever-receding sides.

Stanley Cook.

The Flower I Want

I've drawn a picture for you
Since I myself don't know
Where the flower I want
Is likely to grow.

In the middle it's golden yellow
As the midday sun
And round the middle
A red and a green line run.

The petals have lines of yellow
With red in-between
And the leaves enclose the petals
In a wavy band of green.

Look out for it growing
On a thick black stalk
And bring me one back
Next time you go for a walk.

Art Gallery

The aeroplane has flown away
But I am here and I can draw
The silvery high-flying
Jumbo jet you saw.

I can show you how the ship
And brave explorers look
As they row across the sea
In the story in your book.

Give me the colours and paper
So I can show the starships chase
Each other round the planets
And into outer space.

You can have a row of pictures
Stretching the length of the wall
And high as you can reach
And I will draw them all.

Blue

So much of the world is blue:
Blue as the sea
And ceiling of sky;
Blue in spring as thrush's eggs
In a nest in the hedge,
Blue as bluebells under the trees,
Blue as violets among old leaves;
Blue as mountains far away
Seen through the haze
On a hot summer day;
Blue as the smoke in autumn
From bonfires of branches
In fields and gardens;
Blue as your finger ends
And the tip of your nose
With the winter cold.
How many of the people you know
Look at you
Through eyes of blue?

11

The Hopping Ball

The plastic ball dropped
Plip plop plop
From the counter top
Plip plop plop
To the floor of the toyshop
Plip plop plop
And no one could stop
Plip plop plop
The ball that hopped
Plop plop plop
Out of the shop.

The Ball Game

If you play with a ball in the garden
Everything wants to join in.
It isn't only that the wall
Likes to throw back the ball,
But the long-legged trees
Stick out their wooden knees
Or reach down an arm to send
The ball a way you didn't intend

And piled-up flowerpots in a corner
Fall down and roll all over
And in their hurry to play
Finish by getting in the way.

The ball trips up a sweeping brush
And catches in a currant bush;
Or your mother's clothes prop
Gets a nasty knock
And lets the clothes-line drop
Where, if you are in luck,
She had only dusters pegged up.

Finally the ball
Jumps over the garden wall
To overgrown waste ground,
Hides itself among thick bushes,
Long grass and thistles
And however much you trample round
Refuses to be found.

My Watering-Can

When it's hot I work in the garden
With my plastic watering-can
That's the same shiny red
As a Post Office van.

My watering-can brings rain
When there isn't a cloud in the sky
And gives the flowers a shower
When they are dusty and dry.

I water the grass on the lawn
That the sun has toasted brown;
I water the steps to the lawn
And watch the drops drip down.

I water the path again and again
And make a winding stream;
I sprinkle my motor-car
Until it's perfectly clean.

I water an upturned bucket
And empty flowerpot
And anything that needs to be cooled
When the sun has made it hot.

Dens

Dens are where the bears
Sleep the winter away
Or beasts that hunt by night
Lie hidden in the day
Or a den can be
A quilt or eiderdown
Spread from the settee
Over the back of a chair,
A dark and secret place
Where I have made my lair
And you can come to call on me —
If you dare.

A Tent

A tent is the thinnest house,
So thin you can pack
Its roof and walls
Into one small sack
And take it away
On holiday
Or pitch it on the lawn
When the weather is warm.

16

On the lawn I lie
And close my eyes
So I can dream
My tent is pitched
Beside the rapids
Of a mountain stream
Or in wild Indian country
Out on the lonely prairie
Or deep in a forest
Full of herds of deer
And open my eyes to find
The lawn and garden
Still are here.

Buttons

Buttons pop their heads
Out of button-holes
Early in the morning
To fasten up your clothes.

Putting out a nose
Like a watchful mouse
That doesn't leave its hole
While the cat is in the house,

They peep between the stitching
When they're halfway through
And often then slip back inside
To play a trick on you.

Just when I'm going out
They play their little trick;
I wish that instead of them
I had a zip.

A Knot

Once two pieces of string are knotted
They seem to come alive
And turn to obstinate animals
That refuse to be untied.

Two ends of string wind like snakes
Round and round each other
And the more you pull at one
The tighter they hold together.

If you cut the string with scissors
You've failed to solve the puzzle
And those two stubborn bits of string
Have won the struggle.

19

Hammer and Pincers

A hammer has a hard fist
For punching in the tacks
That hold the carpet fast
To the floor
Or punching nails
Into wooden boards.

But if the nail gets bent
Or the tack doesn't go
Where you meant
You use the pincers
Like a thumb and finger
To pull them out again
And with the hammer
Punch them right
Once more.

Tools make your hand
Extra strong
And your thumb and fingers
Extra long.

The Crane at the Docks

In from the stormy sea come ships
With flags of every colour;
The hooting tugs pull them like toys
Into the calm of the harbour.

The crane sits like a fisherman
At the side of the docks
And lowers a line into a ship
To draw up a heavy box.

All day it fishes with its line
Into the open hatch
And turns to load the waiting lorries
That carry away its catch.

Clouds

Clouds are islands in the sky
No one lives upon,
Over which no birds fly
Or aeroplanes land on.

With mountains deep in snow,
Clouds are islands floating by
That the soft winds blow
Slowly across the sky.

I'll never visit the castles of mist
That from their mountain tops tower up high
Or walk in the ghostly forests
Of the islands in the sky.

The Full Moon

The big full moon shines like a lamp
Hung in the darkness of the night
And the owls and the cats are on the prowl
By its yellow light.

The sun has set that shone for birds to fly
And in its place the moon shines down
On the fox that steals from his lair
And trots towards the town.

The stars are scattered in tiny sparks
But the moon is full and round,
A lamp that shines out brightly
Between white curtains of cloud.

The Star

In the concert of heaven the stars all danced
For the wise old men
And the shepherds' children
But a single star advanced
To the edge of the frosty air
And danced for joy
In reach of the people there
And the baby boy.

Of the millions there are
Which is the star
That turned like a toy
In front of his face
And now is back in its place
High in the sky?

Fog

Fog wraps everything up
And makes it hard to see
The roof of the house
And the top of a tree.

Fog unrolls like cotton-wool
And dims the lights in the street;
It hushes the sound of cars
And people's feet.

Fog is grey as a spider's web
And hides the sun from sight;
Birds perch on hedges and branches
As if already it were night.

Giants Upstairs

The stormy sky turns black as night
And the forked lightning flashes
As if a giant who needed a light
Was striking enormous matches.

From the clouds comes the sound of thunder
As if we had giants upstairs
Who were moving monster furniture
And knocking over tables and chairs.

In the rain above the town
It thunders louder than before
Like a giant falling down
And rolling over and over along the floor.

The Rookery

The rooks are talking of me
As I gaze at them from below
But what they shout to each other
I shall never know.

They flap and hover up above,
Black as bits from a wind-burst umbrella,
And seem annoyed from the sounds they make
As they gather together.

In the treetops where they live
Where no one could come unless he could fly
The rooks are making a great commotion
In their village in the sky.

Living by the River

He hasn't come from town
Just for the afternoon like us
In a car or on a bus:
He lives here.

He walks wet-footed on the rocks
Where the water froths
As it squeezes its way downriver.
Sometimes he stands, sometimes he swims,
But if we're noisy and startle him,
He'll disappear.

He lifts his tail and dips his beak,
Searching the river for something to eat,
And we do our best not to disturb
The explorations of the bird
Who lives here.

The Ants' Nest

The ants that live in the wood,

Brown knobbly insects

Like little beads with legs,

Are gathering specks of food.

More ants are crossing the path
at my feet

Than there are people in our street.

From grains of soil and tiny sticks

They've built themselves a home

As weatherproof and warm

As one made out of bricks.

As many ants are scurrying up and down

As there are people in a town.

Somewhere to Keep Things

It's not that I'm a traveller
Going through the jungle like an explorer
Or up a mountain like a climber,
But I need a case or a backpack
Besides the pockets of my anorak
So that I can safely store away
What I take to school each day,
Something to keep my pencils in,
Rubber, colour sticks and pens.
I work so hard I'd feel too weak
Without an apple and sandwiches to eat;
If it rains at dinnertime I need
A game to play or a comic to read.
I need a place to carry home such things
As a letter about a sponsored swim
And know where I should look
For the model I made and my library book.

The Roundabout

From the park the roundabout
Cuts a magic circle out
I only have to step inside
To get a special kind of ride.

Only a step off the ground,
A push, and I'm flying round,
Turning round non-stop
Like a spinning top.
Another push and I go faster,
Spinning round and speeding past you,
Past a dog standing watching,
Past a grandmother sitting,
Past other children swinging,
Past parked cars outside the railing,
Past someone on top of the climbing-frame.

The roundabout turns and all the same
People and things I passed before
I go past once more,
Past a dog standing watching,
Past a grandmother sitting,
Past other children swinging,
Past parked cars outside the railing,
Past someone on top of the climbing-frame . . .

Sports Day

The weather is hot, the grass is brown
And the sun himself is looking down
And surely he is most impressed
By the way we do our best.

You think that you know how to run
But can you run in wellingtons?
You think that you are very quick
But can you run while you skip?
You'll soon be there, but will it be so soon
If you have to carry an egg on a spoon?
You're sure you won't fall on your back
But how will you manage in a sack?
Are you sure you won't fall on your face
As you stumble along in the three-legged race?

The Egg and Spoon Race

Some people are worrying
About winning the race
But I keep thinking
What a terrible waste
To break an egg
That would make a cake.

I would rather see it
Bouncing up and down
As it boiled in a pan
Than broken on the ground.

I'm keeping my egg as firm
As an acorn in its cup,
Ignoring the people
Shouting 'Hurry up!'

I may be beaten
But my egg can be eaten.

Going by Bus to the Park

The school looked sad today
As it watched us walk away,
Our helper leading the line
And our teacher walking behind.
People everywhere
Stopped their chatting to stare
And nearly everyone
Said they wanted to come.

Our teacher told us to stand
Holding each other's hand
As we waited in the queue
And went in two by two
To the bus for the park
Like animals boarding the Ark.
It *was* a crush
Downstairs on the bus,
Sitting on people's knees
Or four of us squeezed
On a single seat
Crammed like meat
Into a sausage
Or inside a sandwich.
The jerks and jolts at the stops
Made everyone rock
Like shaking toys inside a box,
As bumpy as it used to be
When the Ark was sailing the sea.

The bus-conductor
Unrolled a long white streamer
Of thirty tickets in a row
He gave to me to hold
And the ticket inspector
Said to our teacher
'My word, but you've
Your hands full!'

At the top of the hill
Where the trees can scratch
Their high green backs
Against the clouds,
The blackbirds shout
Across the paths
And daisies are pinned to the grass,
Our teacher counted us
As we got off the bus
Two by two at the park
Like animals leaving the Ark.

Making a Path

Footmarks put together
Wear away the grass
Where people cross the fields
And slowly but surely make a path.

Where people haven't a road
All they need to use
To make themselves a way
Are their boots and shoes.

In crowds along both sides
The flowers stand back
And the tallest bend their heads
Over the narrow track.

Riding my Bicycle

I tread my bicycle pedals
Instead of treading the ground.
The pathway comes towards me
As if it were being wound
Like a rope about a reel
Onto the wheels that I drive round.
I wind my way along the roads
And secret paths I've found.
After my ride of discovery
When once more I'm homeward bound
Everyone knows I'm coming
When they hear my big bell sound.

Feeding the Ducks

When I come to the edge of the pond,
Carrying my bagful of bread,
The ducks can see who's there
And crowd to be fed.
All round the pond they quack
The news that I am back.

Through the air they fly,
Through the water they paddle,
Pushing each other aside,
And along the bank they waddle.
Nowhere else can you see such a rush
Or anyone who fancies bread so much.

Through the Hedge

You squeeze through the hole in the hedge
To come to my house to play
And I squeeze through to go to yours
On another day.

You have a tricycle
With bell and basket for us to ride
Along your concrete path
When we play outside.

When you come to play with me
I have a car with a horn
That warns the cat to watch out
As we speed around the lawn.

You have different pictures on your walls
And different carpets on your floors;
You read new stories in my books
And I read new in yours.

But you like jelly and ice-cream
When you stay to tea
And cakes with icing and cherries on
Just the same as me.

Jelly

The jelly comes quivering
Out of the mould
Like someone shivering
From the cold.

It wibbles and wobbles
Round my plate
As if it were learning
To roller-skate.

Then down my throat
I feel it slide
On the slippery slope
To my inside.

My Birthday Party

At my party it wasn't only
Michael, Diana, Lucy, Clare,
Delroy, Peter, Mary, Bhupa
And all my friends who were there.

Dead lions were there as well
And the quickest to come to life
And leap up from the lawn
With a fearful roar received a prize.

A wolf who knew the time was there,
Turning his face against the wall
Till he reached his dinnertime
And tried to eat us all.

A donkey without a tail was there,
But blindfold how could you know
Which end of him was which
And where he wanted his tail to go?

The party ended: all my friends
And the lions who came to life were gone,
The wolf had had his dinner
And the donkey had got his tail back on.

Bonfire Night

All day like a bonfire
The sun is alight
But glows and goes out
In the cold dark night.

The wind makes fireworks
Of the autumn trees
That scatter showers
Of red and yellow leaves.

And I have a bonfire
That like a fiery dragon
Eats the guy
And roars in the garden.

And I have rockets
That shoot up high
With extra stars
To add to those in the sky.

I use my sparklers
To write my name
And the fireworks paint the night
With coloured flames.

Flower That Opens Only in the Sun

On a cloudy day
The grey sky scowls
And gathers rain
To pelt the children and flowers.

This small wild flower
Folds its petals together
To keep its golden centre
Unharmed by the weather.

A flower so shy
It hides beneath
Its closely folded petals
From the shadow of a leaf.

But when the moody clouds
And the rain have gone by
The flower looks at the sun
With wide-open eye.

The Wild Cherry Tree

The old wild cherry tree
Is like a great white cloud
That caught against the wood
When it came too close to the ground.

In the gusts of the wind
It rocks to and fro
As if it were pushing and pulling
To make the wood let go.

Its blossoms fall in the wind
And in the grass they lie
Like pieces of a broken cloud
That will never return to the sky.

Buds in Autumn

Before the leaves on a tree have fallen
Brown buds with next year's leaves have come;
Leaves and flowers are parcelled up tight
To keep them safe through the winter night,
Snug as fingers and thumb in a glove.

Though the buds may be coated with ice
When winter brings frost and snow
The sun in spring will open them wide
And the leaves and flowers packed inside
Will burst their wrapping and begin to grow.

The Holly Tree

The leaves of the holly tree
Reach right down,
Prickly and shiny green,
To the frosty ground,

Making a spiky wall
No one can get inside
And a tower too tall
For anyone to climb.

This is a tree that keeps
Its scarlet berries out of reach
So hungry birds may eat
However hard it freezes.

The Snowdrop

The snowdrop is not afraid:
It cuts its way out of the ground
With its small green blade.

It holds up to the light
Its slender green-shafted spear
Tipped with splinters of white.

It opens its petals like a lamp
That cannot be put out
By winter's cold and damp.

Lights

Every morning switches on
The golden glow of the sun
And darkness every night
Switches off its light;
But in the street below
Bright street lamps grow,
Planted not in the ground
But in the darkness all around,
As if when the sun had gone
We needed to grow another one,
While in the darkness above us
The stars come out like flowers.

The Waves and the Sandcastle

The waves are attacking my castle
With an angry roar.
Their foaming white horses
Come charging up the shore.

The waves are knocking down
My sandcastle walls.
The tower armoured with seashells
Crumbles and falls.

The waves are winning back
All the beach from the land,
Plucking back the seaweed
And smoothing out the sand.

The waves say castle-building
Is over for today
And they are tidying
The sand and seashells away.

Seashells

The sea has finished with the shells
Its wild waves tore
From their place among the rocks
Deep down in its sandy floor.
The tide goes out and leaves the shells
In a long line upon the shore.

There are shells the shape of petals
Broken from some stone flower
And spiralled shells the shape of horns
Bringing the sea to your ear
Where you hear no more than a whisper
Of the storm that brought them ashore.

At Sea in the House

When I pretend them to be
The table and chairs are land
Where you can safely stand
And the carpet between is sea.

The dining table makes a boat
And I climb on there
By way of the rocking-chair
And out to sea we float.

The pattern in the carpet
Swims like fish on the floor
And anyone opening the door
Is sure to get very wet.

51

The Pet Shop

A biscuity smell comes out
As you open the door of the shop
With its shelves full of tins
And counter of chews and chocolate drops.

The floor in front of the counter
And the room at the back
Are covered almost all over
With well-filled sacks.

There are balls with bells, furry mice,
Powders for this and pills for that
And the Siamese who lives here
Is certainly a lucky cat.

The Doll in the Shop

The doll in the shop stands in a box
Behind a window of cellophane
As if she were staying inside
To shelter from the rain.

While she waits, she wonders
Which of her dresses she ought to wear
To match her bright blue eyes
And the colour of her hair.

She needs someone to tell her
Which of her ribbons to choose,
To button up her coat
And help her fasten her shoes.

Teddy

Teddy keeps warm everywhere
In a coat of honey-coloured fur.
His eyes are bright and brown
And his arms are strong and round.

When first he came he used to speak
In his own kind of squeak
But he lost his voice and his bow
Of yellow ribbon long ago.

Teddy has kicked the straw through his toes
And worn the stitching from his nose
By rubbing me with the end
Like a puppy making friends.

But with his big fat paws
He still drives cars
And railway trains across the floor
Crash into the door.

Looking For Rabbit

I'm searching for Rabbit everywhere:
Under a cushion on the settee
Is a place where Rabbit might be
But when I look he isn't there.

I'm searching for Rabbit everywhere:
The jam-pot's a place where he might hide
If it isn't too sticky for him inside
But when I look he isn't there.

I'm searching for Rabbit everywhere:
He's small enough to crawl
Under the carpet in the hall
But when I look he isn't there.

I'm searching for Rabbit everywhere:
As I sat at the table I felt certain
I saw him hiding behind the curtain
But when I look he isn't there.

I'm searching for Rabbit everywhere:
He might be driving the car away
And going to have a holiday
But when I look he isn't there.

If you see him, tell him I said
It's time for him to go to bed
And underneath my blue blanket
I'm keeping a cosy place for Rabbit.

The Billposter

A clever man, the Billposter,
Going one-handed up his ladder,
Carrying his bucket and brush
And parts of a poster tightly rolled up.

He quickly pastes a space,
Unrolls a sheet he neatly bends
Round his sweeping-brush end
And flips it into place.

Like putting together a jigsaw
He pastes a picture on the wall
And balances while he does that
Like a circus acrobat.
There's no admission fee to pay
To see him performing any day.

The Escape

In the road the mower whirrs,
Cutting the grass that grows at the side,
Pulling like a dog on a lead
With a man holding on behind.

Everywhere it mows the shining grass
And white and yellow flowers fall flat
But a great tall tree grows by the road
And the mower can't mow that.

Round the foot of the tall old tree
Where the noisy mower couldn't go
Tall grass with waving feathers of seed
And the star-shaped flowers grow.

There they are safe and gather round
The foot of the tree in a ring;
The butterflies settle on the flowers
And safely spread their painted wings.

Digging Holes

To dig a hole men come in a van
And stand on the pavement and talk
With orange jackets and helmets on,
Then mark a place on the road with chalk.

The motor they brought behind the van
Starts and chug-chug-chugs non-stop
While the drills hammer-hammer
The top of the road that is hard as rock.

Slowly the men disappear from sight,
Digging deeper into the ground
And walling the hole with pieces of wood
To keep its sides from falling down.

Everyone is digging today
And the badgers, rabbits and moles
That live in the wood beside the road
Need only their paws to dig their holes.

Beside the road the tall trees stand
And deeper than the hole their long roots go:
Among the earth and stones
They wriggle their wooden toes.

Sheba the Cat

The cat-flap bangs back
And the bell on a ribbon round her neck
Gives a tiny ring
As Sheba the cat comes in.

She twists and turns on the table
As if to find her way in a puzzle
And moves among the breakfast things
So softly her bell no longer rings.

Feeling her way with her whiskers
Among the cups and saucers,
She practises guarding the house
And plays at hunting a mouse.

Christmas Cards

Everyone is on the move
On Christmas cards;
Skaters gliding over rivers
The frost has frozen hard,
Kings with golden crowns
Riding their camels towards a star,
Even mice on their sledges
Wearing woolly hats and scarves;
Men in stovepipe hats and long thick coats
Plough a passage through the drifts
In an old-fashioned coach;
Cats sitting in the window
Look out at them in the snow
And robins in holly bushes
Watch them go.
Reindeer whirl Santa Claus
Through a gap in the clouds,
Round and round the chimneys
Towards the roof of our house.

Card Games

Cards tease us by turning their backs
In games like Matching Pairs and Snap,
Lying flat so they can hide
The picture on their other side.

On the table they lie face down,
Never moving or making a sound,
And it's impossible to guess
Which of the pictures will turn up next.

The cards are making fun of me
And when instead of the card I need
I turn up something else
The cards are laughing to themselves.

Jigsaws

A jigsaw is a picture
Cut into little bits.
Put them together so you can know
What dinosaurs there were long ago
Or see the animals embark
In the days of the Flood on Noah's Ark.

See the rocket blast off
On its journey into outer space,
But first you must see each piece
Goes into its proper place.
The elephant doesn't need antlers
Or the deer a trunk, of course,
And it's no good giving the cow
The legs of the horse.

You know the bird can't fly
If it only has one wing,
The sun needs a sky
For shining in,
Without its wheels
A train never goes
And the clown can't breathe
Until you find his nose.

Grandpa's Parcels

Grandpa's parcels have a brown outer skin
Tightly tied with lengths of string,
Strong brown paper that has inside it
Corrugated cardboard or plastic,
Then twists of tissue for padding
And finally fancy wrapping.
Finding the present within one
Is very like peeling an onion.

This is the parcel with my name on
That the Post Office man
Put in a sack that he put in his van,
That he took to the station
Where porters loaded it onto a train
That raced along the rails,
Bearing its bags of mail.
No wonder the parcel
Had to be wrapped up tight
For that long journey through the night.

The Café

When we hadn't a pocket or finger free
To hold more shopping at the store
We all squeezed into the lift
Up to the café on the highest floor.

We found a table with seats for ourselves
And another empty seat
Where we put our shopping to sit
While we had something to eat.

The counter had cakes enough for a party
For us to choose from and take away
And a track of shiny metal bars
Over which we slid our trays.

We drove our trays of cakes like engines
Down the long straight shiny rails
And they joined with other people's
To make a tea-time train.

Eating Outside

As we sit outside the café
The birds fly down from the air;
While we have our snack
They come to claim their share;
Finches search beneath the tables
And a robin perches on a chair.

When one flies to the table
And walks across a tray,
Pecking at bits of biscuit,
No one shoos it away;
We are hungry,
But so are they.

When they have finished
Picnicking with me
Bullfinches and chaffinches
Perch in the nearest tree,
Flying down on the next dropped sandwich
Or scattered crisps that they see.

The Lift

A lift is a room that can't make up its mind
To which of the floors it belongs,
Going down to the basement
And up to the restaurant,

A secret room that most of the time
Hides behind a sliding door
And travels with a whistling sound
Out of sight from floor to floor.

Is it furniture or food,
Clothes or toys it is looking for
While from morning to night
It searches up and down the store?

Going Away

At Christmas when we go
To Grandma's to stay
Or when we go to the seaside
For a summer holiday,
Who is there to mind
All the things I have left behind,
Some in a box, some in a cot,
Some put away, some on a tray,
Some by themselves, some piled on shelves?

The sun keeps his eye on every one,
Sometimes taking a hurried look
Round the edge of a cloud,
Sometimes staring hours
At the picture on a book.
He watches plants grow tall
In pots on the window-sill
And goes to see himself
In the mirror on the wall
And sometimes he shines in the eye
Of a toy that is sitting still
And it winks in reply.

The Vacuum Cleaner

Press a switch with your finger or foot
And the vacuum cleaner gathers a harvest
From the wide field of the carpet
Of yesterday's litter and dust.

Fallen birdseed and bits of grit,
Hairgrips and twisted pins
That bounce and rattle inside it
Make a bagful for the bin.

It finds beneath your feet
A thread of cotton, a cornflake,
A wrapper without a sweet
And the last iced crumb of a cake.

Like a detective looking for clues
It gathers from the floor
Each little thing that proves
What happened the day before.

The Tea Table

The table is some strange animal
Hiding beneath the tablecloth
And keeping perfectly still
So none of the tea things fall off.

The table where we are having tea
Stands up on four straight legs
And somewhere under the tablecloth
It has tucked in its wooden head.

It carries the saucers, cups and plates
And the teapot on a mat
And when there is time to spare
It likes you to polish its back.

The Hat of the House

Houses have roofs like hats
To keep out rain and snow
And cover their heads
When strong winds blow.

From under the hat of the house
Windows stare like eyes
At the passing clouds
And wink at the sun in the sky.

Through the hat of the house
The chimneys stick
Like long red ears
Made out of brick.

On the hat of the house
Tired birds take a rest
Or under its edges
Build their nests.

Holes for ears
And birds' nests in a hat —
Not many people
Have hats like that!

In the Bath

Out of the taps two rushing rivers,
One hot, one cold, bubble and splash
And like the sea when the tide comes in
The water creeps along the bath.

A yellow duck swims out to sea
Beside a sky-blue boat,
A curly orange fish
Nibbles at my toes
And I am an island in the sea
With warm waves washing over me.

Going to Bed

It took a long time to wash away
The grubby marks I got today —
Brown from the chocolates I ate,
The black from reading the paper
And red from the picture I painted —
And then my arms got lost
Inside my pyjama top.
It makes me hungry standing there
While you brush my hair,
So now that at last you've fixed it
May I have a biscuit?

My throat's as dry as a desert
From standing there so long,
So please may I have a drink —
Just a little one?
I've had a story about a dog,
It wouldn't be fair after that
Not to have one about a cat.
Can't you make up one
About a cat who was clever and strong
And stayed awake all night long?
Was it 'Brush your teeth' you said?
I'm feeling terribly tired
And must get into bed.

Index of first lines